D1432730

Mommy wakes up with eyes that are red
To the sound of a little beside her bed
"Mommy! Mommy! Turn on the TV!
I need milk! I need to pee!
Mommy, please open the bathroom door!
Mommy, Mommy, my ear feels sore!
Mommy! Mommy! Mommy!"

Shh... Mommy needs a moment!

Mommy!!

Mommy!!!

Mommy!!!!

Shhh... Mommy needs a moment!

With looks of confusion, the littles ran away.
Around the corner, Mommy heard them say
"What's wrong with Mommy?
Did we make her sad?
Should we cheer her up
Since we were being bad?

Mommy peeked around the corner
And Mommy saw, to her horror
Two littles with her lipstick in hand
Making art on the wall, along with glue and sand.
"I love you Mommy" was proudly displayed.
The littles were sure Mommy would love what they'd made.

Mommy's eyes started twitching
And her head became hot
The littles grinned at her
Not knowing they had been caught.

Mommy was just about to shout
The littles noticed, not knowing what about.
And then Mommy paused, before she exploded
Sister turned to brother, and quietly noted

Shhh... Mommy needs a moment!

Without a word, Mommy turned around.
She picked up the mug of coffee she'd found.
Which was now cold, so she began to heat it.
"Everything is fine! It's all fine!" She repeated.

She let out a huge sigh, and then sat down.
And in under a minute, two littles came around.
"Mommy! You didn't get my milk yet."
"Mommy! I need juice! Did you forget?"
Mommy's eyes got big, and her head drooped.
And just then a little piped, "Mommy, I pooped!"

And then Mommy laughed to keep from crying.
The littles, however, then started whining.
"Mommy! Mommy! You need to get up."
"Mommy! Mommy! Where's my sippy cup?"

So Mommy got up to get them what they needed.
But when she tried to sit down again, she was greeted
By a little with big tears in his eyes
She sat up quickly with great surprise.

"Mommy," he said. "I feel so sad."
"Mommy, I'm so sorry I was bad."
Then Mommy scooped him up
And wrapped him in a hug.
And Mommy rocked him
All snug like a bug.

"My baby," she said, to her little boy.
"You and your sister bring me so much joy.
But sometimes, we all get emotions
That get really, really big like oceans.

Mommy isn't perfect, and neither are you.
Sometimes we all need a moment--or two.
Mommy loves you, and can't stay mad all day.
Why don't we go sit down and play.

And just like that, they all felt better.
Mommy forgot all that had upset her.
She smiled at her littles, because they were so smart.
They knew that they held the key to her heart.

They had ups and downs as the day passed.
But Mommy knew they were growing up fast,
Mommy did her best to soak up it all.
And enjoy every moment--big and small.

ABOUT THE AUTHOR

Jordan Rios is a teacher, a life coach, and a course creator. She is a wife and a mom of six littles. She loves to go hiking, journal, paint, and learn languages. She lives with her family in Tennessee.

www.jordanmrios.com

Made in the USA
Columbia, SC
18 March 2022

57863911R00015